D0267559

DK

ANGRY BIRDS
STAR WARS

Darth Swindle's Secrets

Written by Scarlett O'Hara

LONDON, NEW YORK, MUNICH,
MELBOURNE AND DELHI

Editorial Assistant Ruth Amos
Senior Editor Hannah Dolan
Designer Richard Horsford
Jacket Designer Rhys Thomas
Pre-Production Producer Rebecca Fallowfield
Producer Danielle Smith
Managing Editor Laura Gilbert
Design Manager Maxine Pedliham
Art Director Ron Stobbart
Publishing Manager Julie Ferris
Publishing Director Simon Beecroft

Reading Consultant
Maureen Fernandes

Lucasfilm
Executive Editor J. W. Rinzler
Art Director Troy Alders
Keeper of the Holocron Leland Chee
Director of Publishing Carol Roeder

Rovio
Approvals Editor Nita Ukkonen
Senior Graphic Designer Jan Schulte-Tigges
Publishing and Licensing Manager
Laura Nevanlinna
Vice President of Book Publishing
Sanna Lukander

First published in Great Britain in 2013 by
Dorling Kindersley Limited
80 Strand, London WC2R 0RL

10 9 8 7 6 5 4 3 2 1
001-196556-Nov/13

A CIP catalogue record for this book
is available from the British Library.

ISBN: 978-1-40934-398-1

Colour reproduction by Altaimage, UK
Printed and bound in China by L-Rex

Discover more at
www.dk.com
www.starwars.com

Contents

4 Criminal mastermind
6 The Pork Side
8 Brave birds
10 Copypigs
12 Pig Lords
14 Grunter's gang
16 Frightened fowl
18 Jedi enemies
20 Dark pig power
22 Bounty hunters
24 Crazy warrior
26 Moar's mission
28 Tempting trick
30 Watch out for the birds!
32 Glossary

DK

ANGRY BIRDS
STAR WARS
II

Darth Swindle's Secrets

Written by Scarlett O'Hara

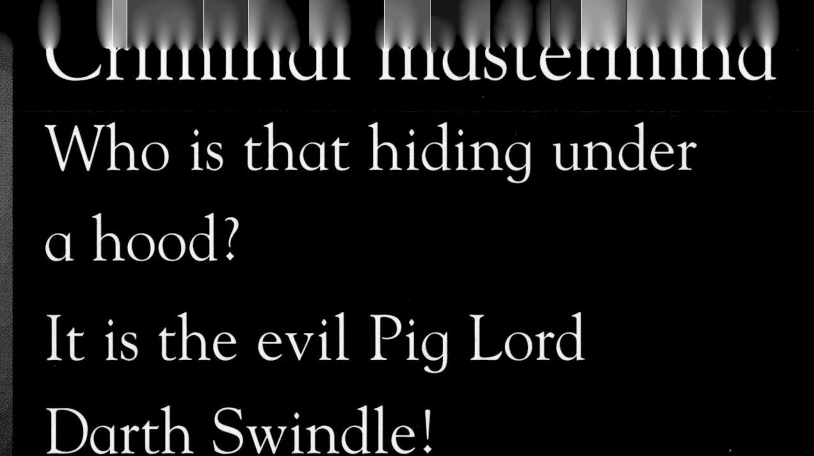

Criminal mastermind

Who is that hiding under a hood?

It is the evil Pig Lord Darth Swindle!

He has lots of nasty secrets.

Evil grin

Hidden weapon

Swindle wants to rule the galaxy and eat all the sweets and junk food.

His snout is good for smelling out food.

snout

The Pork Side

A lot of pigs are on sneaky Swindle's side.

It is called the Pork Side.

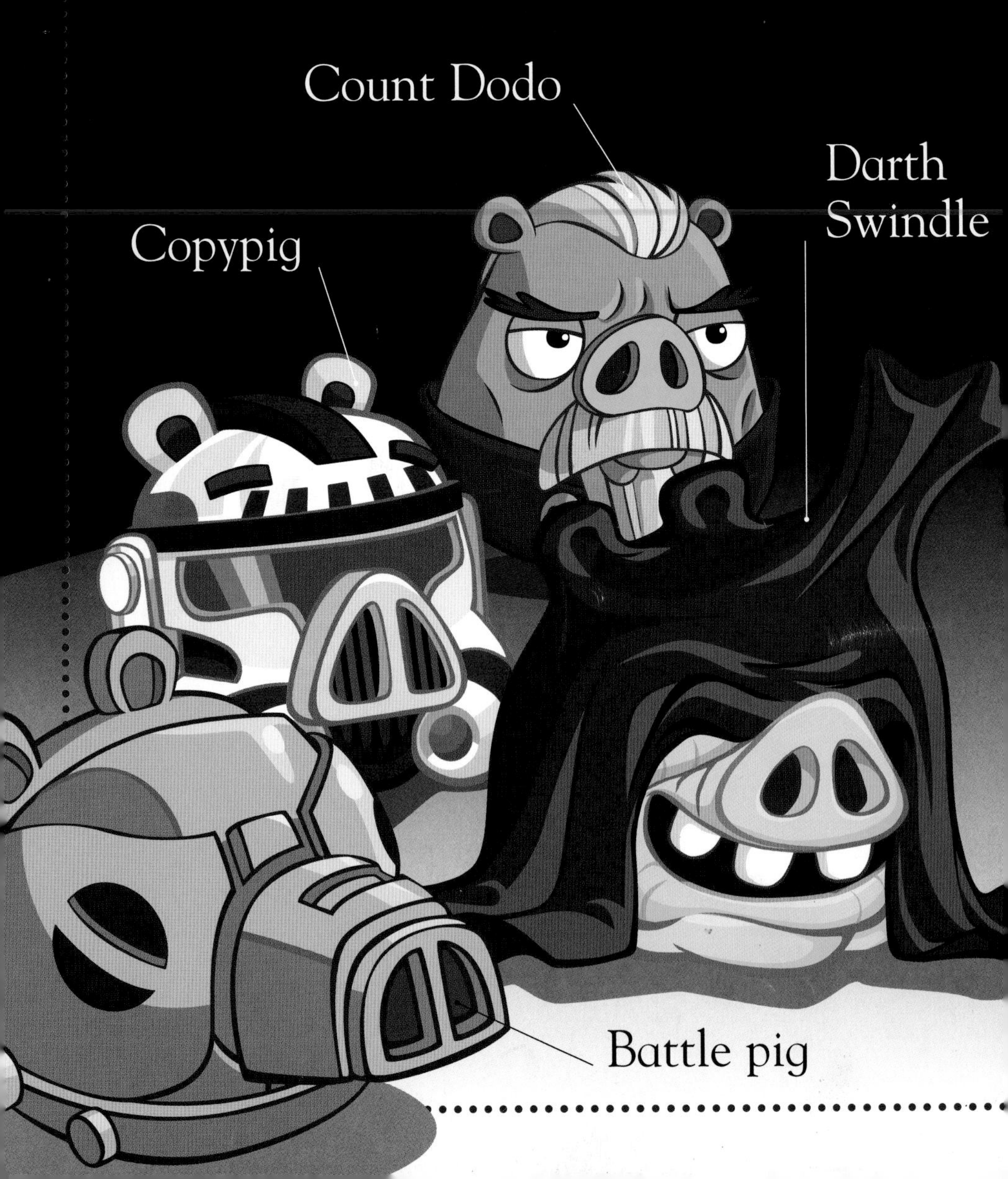
Count Dodo
Darth Swindle
Copypig
Battle pig

The pigs want to eat all the junk food! They also want to find The Egg, which has the power to rule the galaxy.

Warhog
Darth Moar
General Grunter

Brave birds

Here are the good birds!
Some of the birds
are Jedi Bird warriors.
They are brave fighters.

C–3PYOLK
Moa Windu
Obi-Wan
Kaboomi
Quail-Gon

Only Yoda Bird knows where to find The Egg.
It is disguised as R2-EGG2.
Don't tell Darth Swindle!

R2-EGG2
Queen Peckmé
Redkin Skywalker
Jar Jar Wings
Yoda Bird

Copypigs

Watch out! Darth Swindle has an army of Copypigs. He orders them to search the galaxy for sweets.

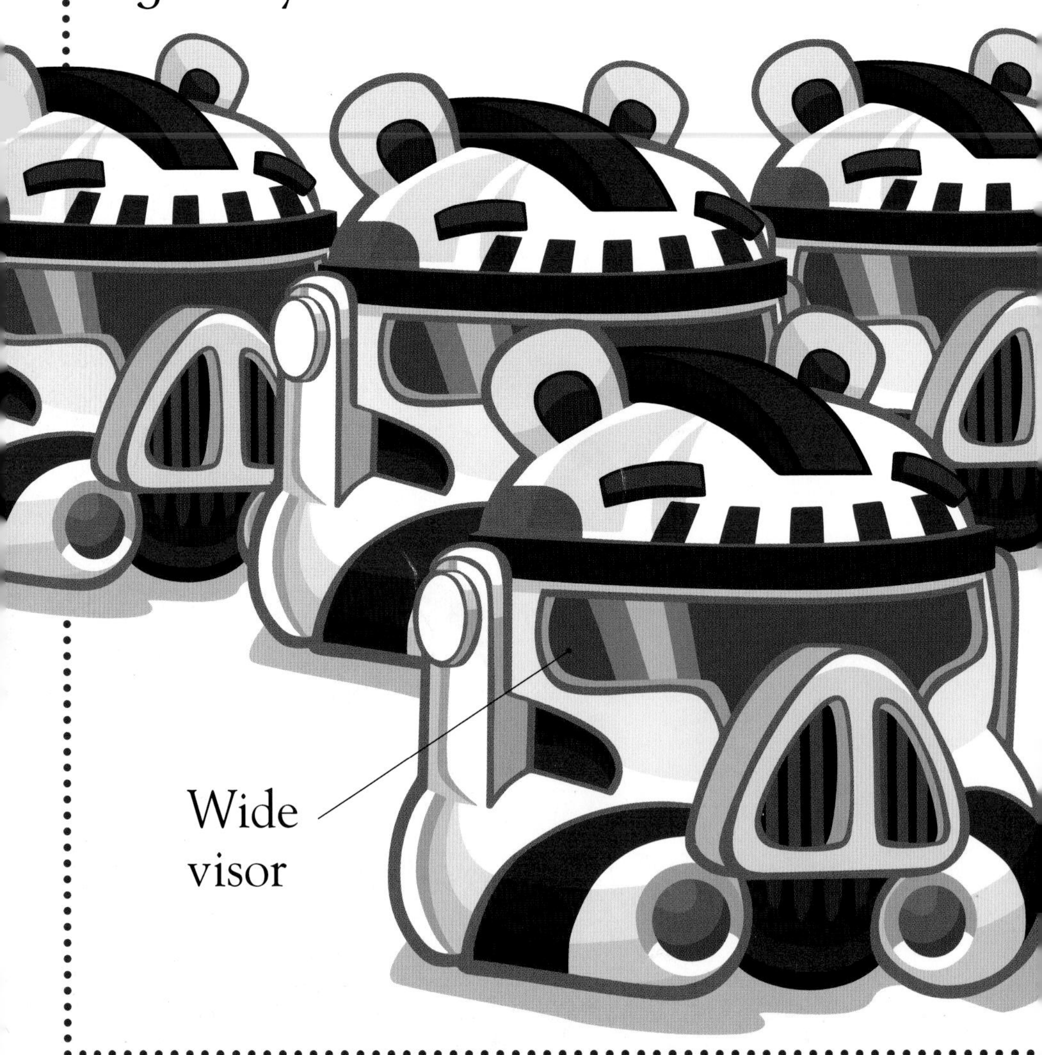
Wide visor

The Copypigs are very stupid.
They do not understand
Swindle's greedy orders.
They copy one another
and get confused!

Piggy
ears

Sleek
grey hair
Snooty
face

Pig Lords

Darth Swindle commands several pesky Pig Lords.

Count Dodo used to be a Jedi. Now he is a horrible hog!

Fierce General Grunter's body is made out of metal. He fights with four lightsabers!

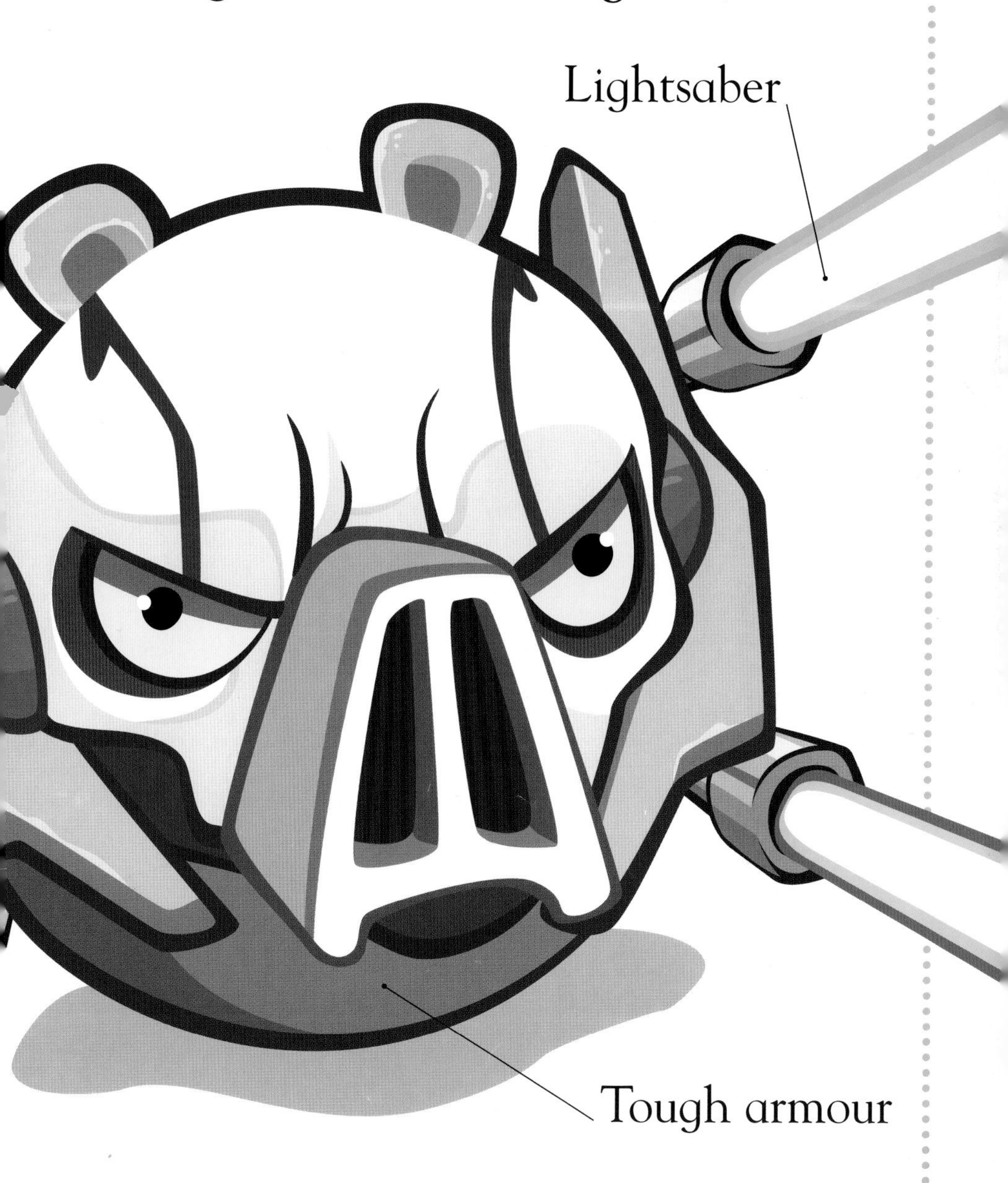
Lightsaber
Tough armour

Grunter's gang

General Grunter leads an army of droids.

Battle pigs are not very bright because their programming went wrong!

droids
Long snout

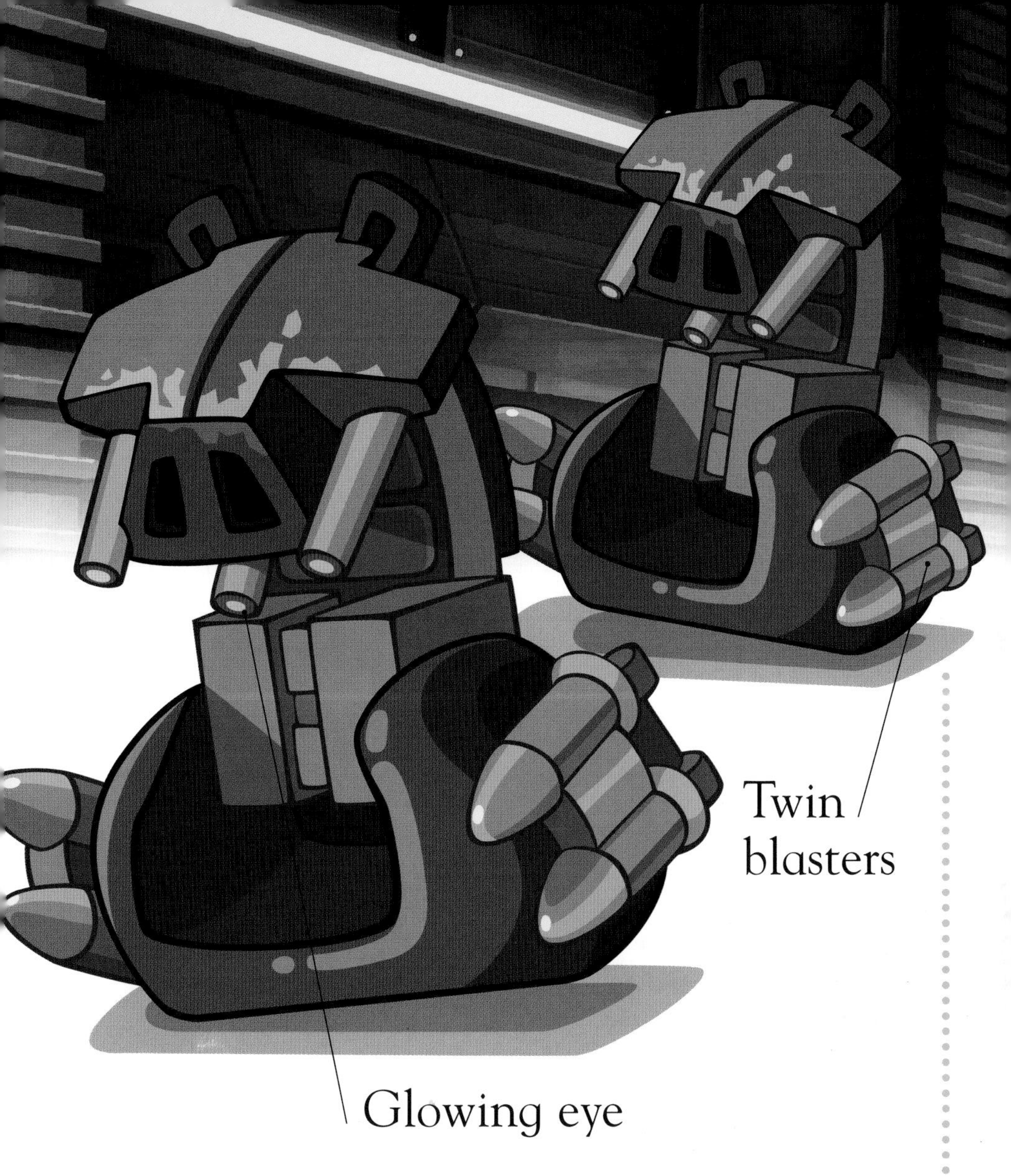
Twin blasters
Glowing eye

The Warhogs are very fast and have lots of weapons. Everybody is scared of them – even the Jedi Birds.

Frightened fowl

Goofy Jar Jar Wings and loyal Terebacca are in big trouble!

Furry feathers
Tough metal shell
Eyes on stalks

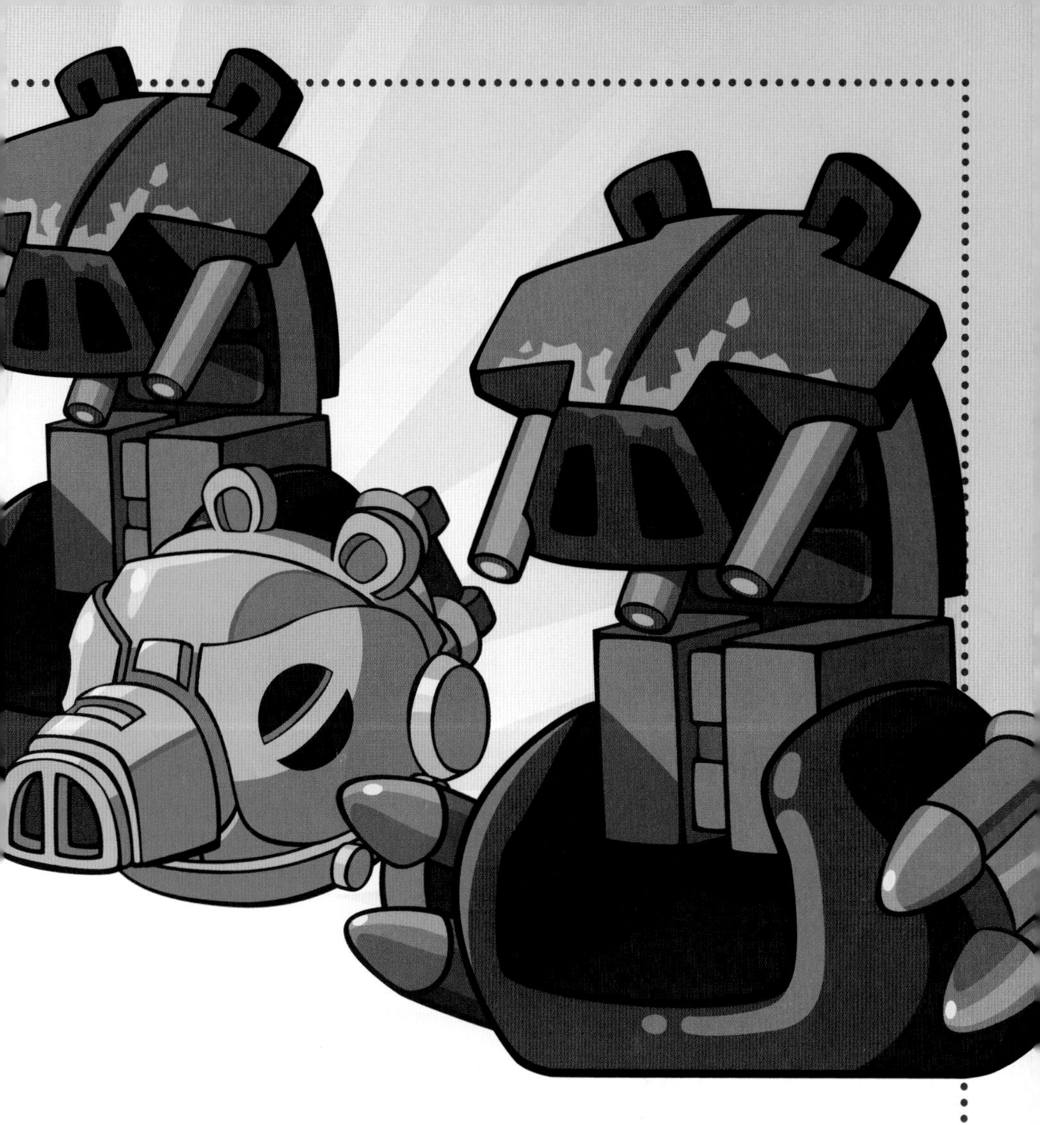

Darth Swindle thinks they have hidden food from him.

Swindle sends in his droids to teach them a lesson.

Jedi enemies

Darth Swindle has many enemies.

One enemy is the Jedi Bird Moa Windu.

Bushy brow
Glowing lightsaber

Moa is a great lightsaber fighter.

The wise Jedi Yoda Bird
and Moa talk together.
How can they stop Swindle?

Wise wrinkled
forehead

Dark pig power

Darth Swindle challenges
Moa to a duel.
Sly Swindle wants to defeat
Moa and rule the roost!

Pow! Swindle zaps Moa with his Force lightning.

Force lightning

The wicked pig wins the fight.

Jedi cloak

Bounty hunters

Darth Swindle sends these bounty hunters to capture enemy birds.

Zam Weasel uses electro-goggles to find her target.

Zam's electro-goggles

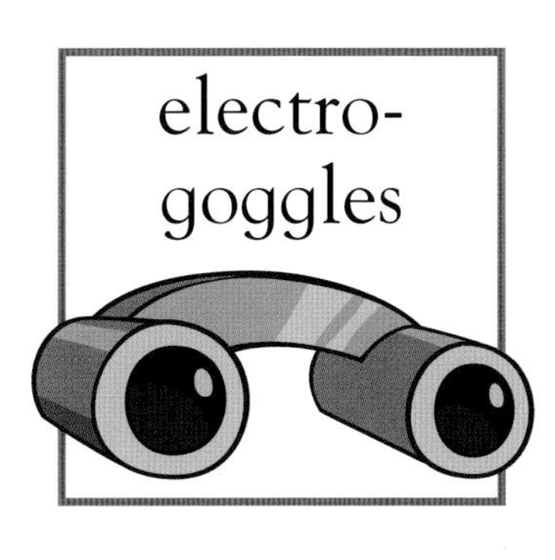
electro-
goggles

Cunning Jango Fatt uses a jet pack to escape from trouble.

Jango's jet pack

Crazy warrior

Watch out for this crazy pig!
His name is Darth Moar.

He is Darth Swindle's
pig apprentice.

Head
horn
Evil
grin

Moar joined the Pork Side when he was young.

Swindle tempted him with lots of junk food.

Staring eyes

Moar's mission

Darth Swindle sends his apprentice on missions.

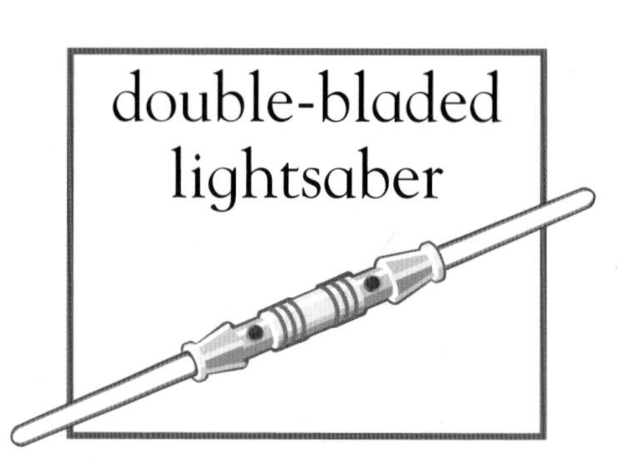
double-bladed lightsaber

Moar has a double-bladed lightsaber.

Look! Darth Moar is trying to capture Queen Peckmé.

Quail-Gon and Obi-Wan try to stop him.

Powerful blade
Green bird lightsaber

Sharp beak
Battle scar

Tempting trick

Darth Swindle is a very sly pig. He tries to tempt Jedi Birds over to the Pork Side.

Swindle tempts Redkin Skywalker to join the pigs.

Redkin becomes the Pig Lord Lard Vader.

Huge helmet

Watch out for the birds!

These birds won't let
Darth Swindle win.
They will fight back.

They will work together
to beat the evil Pork Side.
They will stop the pigs from
finding The Egg....

Glossary

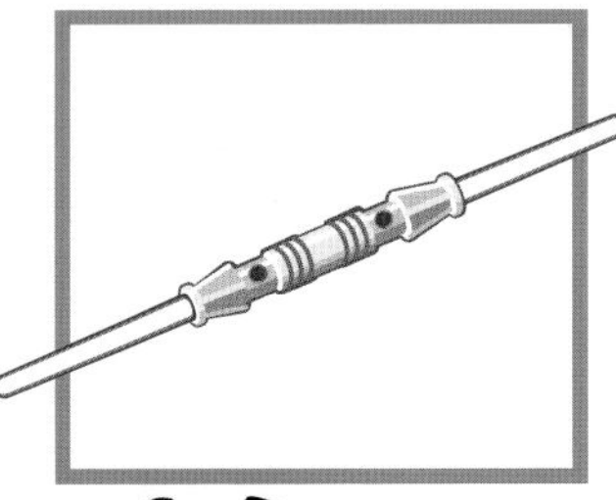

Double-bladed lightsaber
A weapon with a beam of energy at each end.

Droids
A type of robot, like battle pigs or Warhogs.

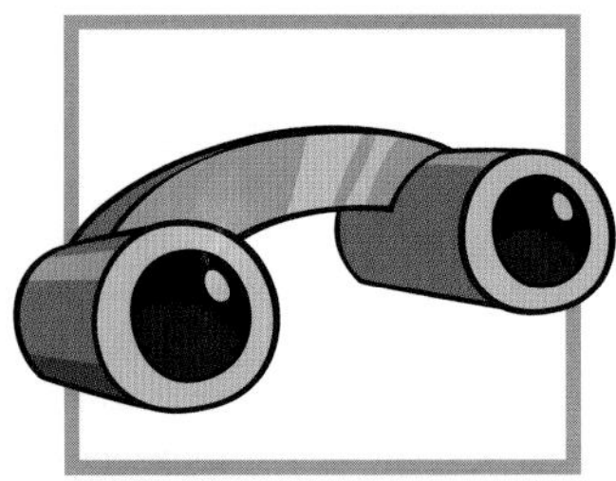

Electro-goggles
Goggles used to spy on a person or thing.

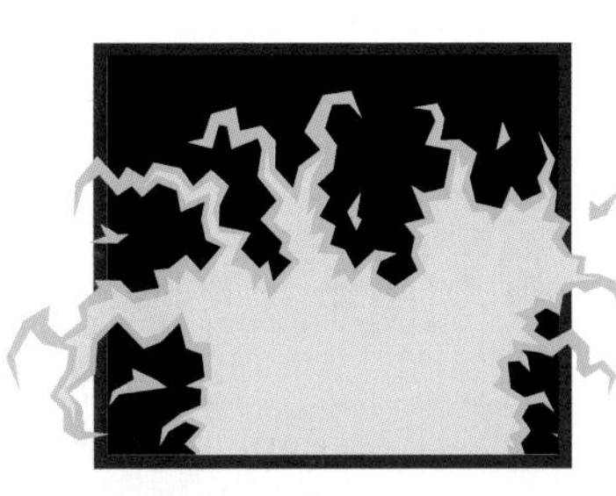

Force lightning
A deadly power that only Pig Lords use.

Snout
A round, flat nose that some animals have.

Index

battle pig
6, 14
Copypig
6, 10–11
Count Dodo
6, 12
Darth Moar
7, 24–25, 27
Darth Swindle
4–5, 6, 9, 10,
12, 17, 18,
19, 20, 21,
22, 24, 26,
28, 30
General
Grunter
7, 13, 14
Jango Fatt
23
Jedi Bird
8, 15, 18, 28
lightsaber
13, 19, 26, 27
Moa Windu
18, 20, 21
Pig Lord
4, 12–13, 29
Pork Side
6–7, 25, 28,
31
Warhog
7, 15
Zam Weasel
22